COUNTING
FARM

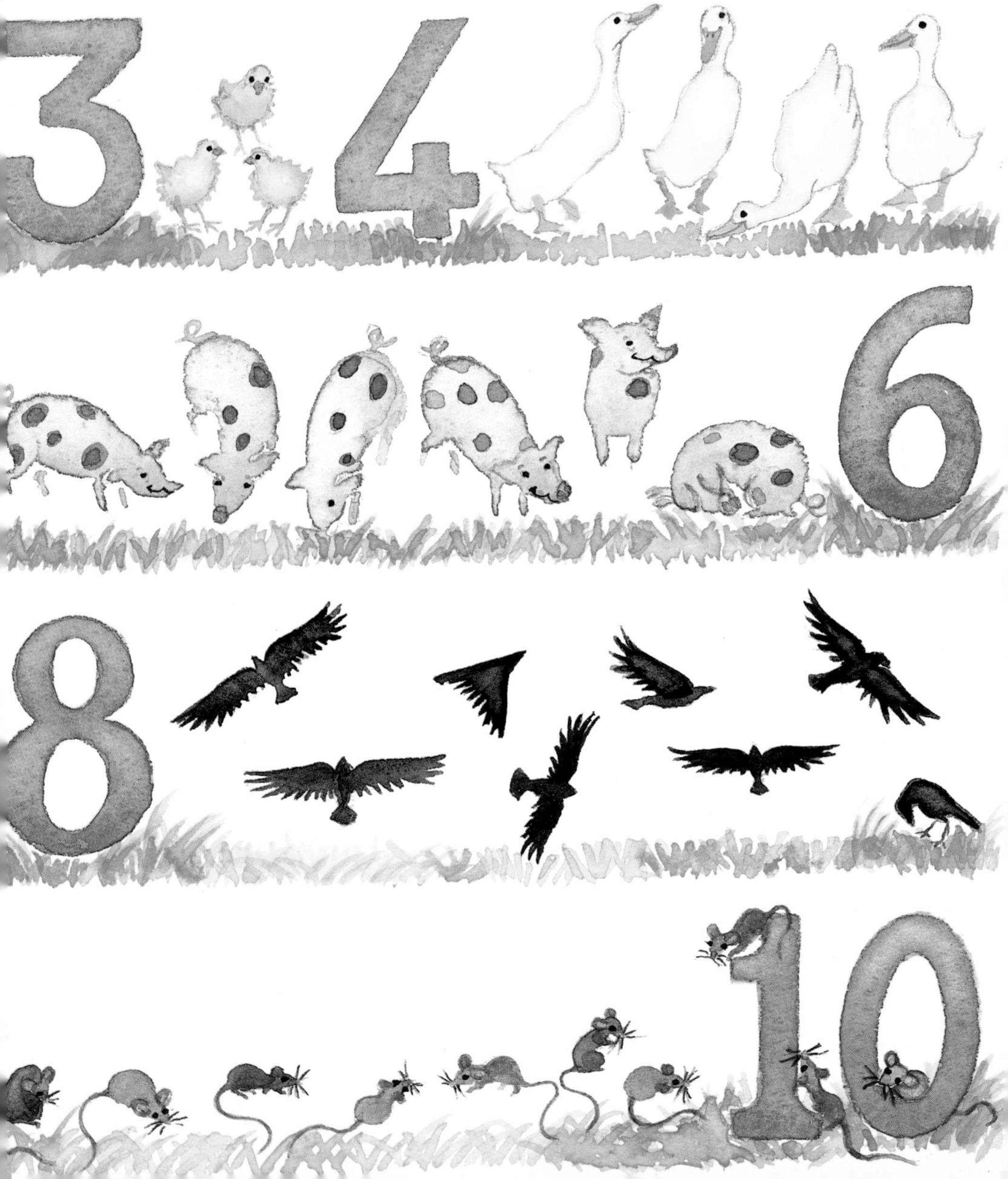
3
4
6
8
10

First published 1995 by Walker Books Ltd
87 Vauxhall Walk, London SE11 5HJ

This edition published 2009

2 4 6 8 10 9 7 5 3 1

This book has been typeset in Garamond Educational

Printed in China

British Library Cataloguing in Publication Data:
a catalogue record for this book is available from the British Library.

ISBN 978-0-7445-3556-3

www.walker.co.uk

Counting Farm

Kathy Henderson

WALKER BOOKS
AND SUBSIDIARIES
LONDON · BOSTON · SYDNEY · AUCKLAND

One cockerel

Two speckled hens

Three little chicks
in the poultry pen

Four ducks

Five brown cows

Six little
pigs and
a mother
sow

Seven
white sheep

Eight
black crows

Nine little lambs
skipping on their toes

And playing in the
hay at the back of
the barn there are
ten little mice on
Counting Farm.